Science
Olympiad

Highly useful for all school students participating
in various Olympiads & Competitions

Series Editor Keshav Mohan
Author Reena Kar

Class
1

arihant

ARIHANT PRAKASHAN, MEERUT

ARIHANT PRAKASHAN, MEERUT
All Rights Reserved

ꫝ **Administrative & Production Offices**

Regd. Office   'Ramchhaya' 4577/15, Agarwal Road, Darya Ganj New Delhi -110002
Tele: 011- 47630600, 43518550; Fax: 011- 23280316

Head Office   Kalindi, TP Nagar, Meerut (UP) - 250002
Tele: 0121-2401479, 2512970, 4004199; Fax: 0121-2401648

All disputes subject to Meerut (UP) jurisdiction only.

ꫝ **Sales & Support Offices**

Agra, Ahmedabad, Bengaluru, Bhubaneswar, Bareilly, Chennai, Delhi, Guwahati, Haldwani, Hyderabad, Jaipur, Jhansi, Kolkata, Kota, Lucknow, Meerut, Nagpur & Pune

ꫝ **ISBN**   978-93-5094-414-1

ꫝ **Price**   ₹50.00

Typeset by Arihant DTP Unit at Meerut
Printed & Bound by Arihant Publications (I) Ltd. (Press Unit)

Production Team

Publishing Manager	Amit Verma	*Page Layouting*	Ravi Saini & Shravan Pandey
Project Coordinator	Shelly Singhal	*Figure Illustrator*	Brahampal Singh
Cover Designer	Syed Darin Zaidi	*Proof Reader*	Rachi Aggarwal
Inner Designer	Ravi Negi		

For further information about Arihant Books
log on to www.arihantbooks.com or email to info@arihantbooks.com

Preface

CONTENTS

Science Olympiad Series for Class 1st-10th is a series of books which will challenge the young inquisitive minds by the non-routine and exciting problems based on concept of Science.

The main purpose of this series is to make the students ready for competitive exams. The school/board exams are of qualifying nature but not competitive, they do not help the students to prepare for competitive exams, which mainly have objective questions.

- **Need of Olympiad Series**
  This series will fill this gap between the School/Board and Competitive exams as this series have all questions in objective format. This series helps students who are willing to sharpen their problem solving skills. Unlike typical assessment books, which emphasis on drilling practice, the focus of this series is on practicing problem solving techniques.

- **Development of Logical Approach**
  The thought provoking questions given in this series will help students to attain a deeper understanding of the concepts and through which students will be able to impart Reasoning/Logical/Analytical skills in themselves.

- **Complement Your School Studies**
  This series complements the additional preparation needs of students for regular school/board exams. Along with, it will also address all the requirements of the students who are approaching National/State level Olympiads.

I shall welcome criticism from the students, teachers, educators and parents. I would also like to hear from all of you about errors and deficiencies, which may have remained in this edition and the suggestions for the next edition.

Editor

OLYMPIAD Class 1

CONTENTS

OLYMPIAD Class1

1

Living and Non-Living Things

1. Identify the non-living thing.

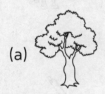 (a)    (b)    (c)   (d)

2. Which of the following is the living thing?

 (a)    (b)   (c)    (d)

3. Cow eats grass as cow is a _____

(a) Living thing   (b) Non-living thing

(c) Bird   (d) Toy

4. Which among the following will grow in size?

 (a)   (b)    (c)   (d)

5. Living things produce babies. Which picture shows that?

(a)    (b)   (c)    (d)

6. Which of the following does NOT belong to the group formed by the others?

(a)   (b)    (c)    (d)

7. Which among the following will move on its own?

(a)   (b)   (c)   (d)

8. In the given pictures identify the living things.

   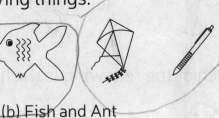

(a) Aeroplane and Kite   (b) Fish and Ant

(c) Pen and fish   (d) Aeroplane and pen

9. Which of the following is correct?

(a) Living things cannot move   (b) Non-living things can move on their own

(c) Living things grow   (d) Non-living things need food to live

10. A can run, but a _____ cannot.

(a)   (b)   (c)    (d)

11. _____ is non-living thing but _____ is living thing.

    (a) Bird, goat   (b) Dog, Aeroplane (c) Book, Bird   (d) Bird, Book

12. In the given picture, identify the thing that has life.

    (a) Tree   (b) Road   (c) Mountain   (d) Car

13. Living things need _____ to live.

    (a) paper   (b) sky   (c) air   (d) fan

14. Which action shows that living things breathe?

(a)   (b)    (c)    (d)

15. From the given picture, what do you know about living things?

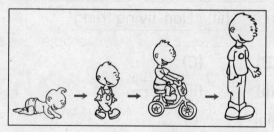

    (a) Living things move   (b) Living things breathe

    (c) Living things reproduce   (d) Living things grow

16. Select the odd one out.

(a)   (b)   (c)    (d)

17. Which word in these boxes is under the wrong heading?

Living Things	Non-Living Things
Rose Plant	Hindi Book
Peacock	Mango Tree
Elephant	Blue Pen

(a) Elephant   (b) Rose plant   (c) Mango Tree   (d) Hindi book

18. All living things need Air, _____ and Food to live.

(a) Water   (b) Grass   (c) Apple   (d) Land

19. Which of the following lives in water?

(a)   (b)   (c)    (d)

20. Match the Column I with Column II.

	Column I		Column II
(A)	Peacock	(i)	Need air and water
(B)	Box	(ii)	Living thing
(C)	Living things	(iii)	Non-living thing

	(A)	(B)	(C)
(a)	(i)	(ii)	(iii)
(b)	(ii)	(iii)	(i)
(c)	(iii)	(i)	(ii)
(d)	(i)	(iii)	(ii)

21. Which of these natural things is living?

(a) 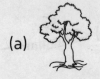   (b)   (c) 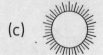   (d)

22. Which is a natural non-living thing?

(a)    (b)   (c)   . (d)

23. Identify the living things and choose the correct option.

(a) Shoes, Cow, Moon, Man   (b) Cow, Frog, Man, Bird

(c) Phone, Bird, House, Cow   (d) Moon, Drum, Man, Frog

24. Given picture shows a boy and a cycle. Which of the statement is not true?

(a) Both boy and cycle can move   (b) Boy can move on its own

(c) Cycle can move on its own   (d) Boy has life while cycle is lifeless

25. Which of the following things cannot live without food?

(a) A bulb   (b) A Plant   (c) An Aeroplane   (d) A Pencil box

26. Which of the following observations have been wrongly paired?

	Column I		Column II
1.	A cat drinks water	(i)	Hungry
2.	A Hen lays eggs	(ii)	Reproduce
3.	A leaf turns yellow and falls from a tree	(iii)	Dies
4.	Rohan eats food	(iv)	Thirsty

(a) Only 2   (b) Only 1   (c) 1 and 2   (d) 1 and 4

2

Plants

1. Very big plants with wooden stems are called _____ .

(a) Climbers   (b) Creepers   (c) Trees   (d) Shrubs

2. Pick the odd one out.

(a)    (b)   (c)   (d)

3. I comes from a shrub and people like to drink me. Who am I?

(a)  Tea   (b) Ghee   (c) Milk   (d) Coke

4. Which of the following is not a foodgrain?

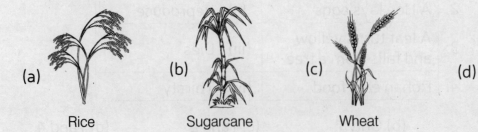

(a)   (b)   (c)   (d)

Rice   Sugarcane   Wheat   Maize

5. Given figure shows seed of which fruit?

(a) Papaya   (b) Lemon   (c) Plum   (d) Mango

Direction (6-8) See the picture given below and answer the questions.

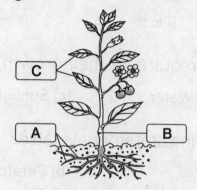

6. I hold the plant. I am present under the ground.

(a) Fruit   (b) Flower   (c) Root   (d) Stem

7. I support the plant. Leaves, fruits, flowers grows on me.

(a) Stem   (b) Root   (c) Seed   (d) Bud

8. I am the kitchen of the plant as I make food for it.

(a) Root   (b) Fruit   (c) Stem   (d) Leaves

9. Which of the following fruit is from a creeper?

(a)
Apple

(b)
Orange

(c)
Watermelon

(d)
Banana

10. Which vegetable is the root of the plant?

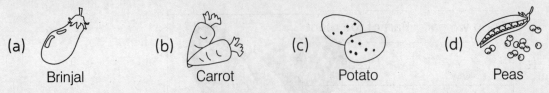

(a) Brinjal   (b) Carrot   (c) Potato   (d) Peas

11. Pick the odd one out.

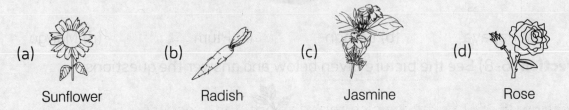

(a) Sunflower   (b) Radish   (c) Jasmine   (d) Rose

12. What do the plants require for their growth?

(a) Air   (b) Water   (c) Sunlight   (d) All of these

13. Which of the following statement is false?

(a) Cherry is a fruit   (b) Potato is a vegetable

(c) Rice is a grain   (d) Groundnut is a spice

14. These are seeds . From where do we get them?

(a) Flowers   (b) Fruits   (c) Roots   (d) Leaves

15. _____ has just one seed in it but _____ has many seeds in it.

(a) Mango, Banana   (b) Orange, Guava

(c) Papaya, Mango   (d) Mango, Papaya

16. Arrange the pictures in order starting from seed to tree.

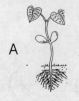

A   B   C   D

(a) B D A C   (b) D A C B   (c) A B D C   (d) C B D A

17. Which of these is incorrectly matched?

	Food we eat	Part of the plant
(a)		Leaf
(b)		Root
(c)		Stem
(d)		Fruit

Direction (18-19) Look at the picture and answer the questions.

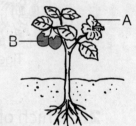

18. The part of a plant at point A is _____.

    (a) Grass   (b) Fruit

    (c) Leaf   (d) Flower

19. _____ is formed in B.

    (a) Fruit   (b) Root   (c) Stem   (d) Leaf

20. Which of the following fruits give us oil?

    (a)   (b)   (c)   (d)

       Apple   Mango   Coconut   Cherry

21. Find the correct number of fruits, flowers and vegetables from the box.

Pumpkin	Apple	Potato	Guava	Brinjal
Ladyfinger	Lotus	Orange	Cucumber	

    (a) 2 fruits, 3 vegetables, 2 flowers   (b) 6 vegetables, 3 fruits, 2 flowers

    (c) 5 vegetables, 3 fruits, 1 flower   (d) 3 vegetables, 3 fruits, 3 flowers

3

Animals

1. Which of the following is not a wild animal?

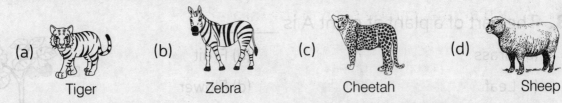

(a) Tiger　　(b) Zebra　　(c) Cheetah　　(d) Sheep

2. Which of the following is not a pet/domestic animal?

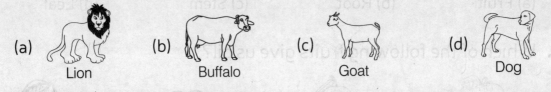

(a) Lion　　(b) Buffalo　　(c) Goat　　(d) Dog

3. Which is the largest animal in the world?

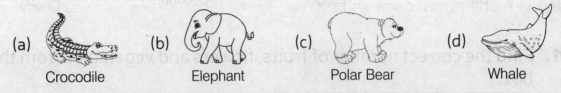

(a) Crocodile　　(b) Elephant　　(c) Polar Bear　　(d) Whale

4. Which of the following is not a water animal?

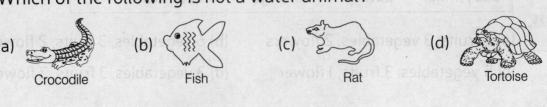

(a) Crocodile　　(b) Fish　　(c) Rat　　(d) Tortoise

5. Which animal can walk easily on sand?

(a)
Camel

(b)
Horse

(c)
Donkey

(d)
Bear

6. Which of the following cannot fly?

(a)
Sparrow

(b)
Crow

(c)
Squirrel

(d)
Parrot

7. Which animal can be seen in the farms?

(a)
Stag

(b)
Ox

(c)
Monkey

(d)
Fox

8. Which of the following is not an insect?

(a)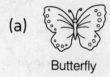
Butterfly

(b)
Ant

(c)
Lizard

(d)
Grasshopper

9. Which animal can run fast?

(a)
Deer

(b)
Cheetah

(c)
Ostrich

(d)
Tiger

10. Which animal lives on trees?

(a) Monkey   (b) Donkey   (c) Elephant   (d) Fish

11. There are some birds that cannot fly. Which of these birds cannot fly?

Pigeon (1) Owl (2) Ostrich (3) Kiwi (4) Parrot (5) Penguin (6)

(a) 2, 3 and 4   (b) 1, 2 and 6   (c) 4, 5 and 6   (d) 3, 4 and 6

12. Where do wild animals live?

(a) Homes   (b) Farms   (c) Forests   (d) Villages

13. Which of the following is not correctly match?

(a) Birds – Grain   (b) Lion—Flesh

(c) Deer—Both plants and flesh   (d) Cow—Grass

14. What does cow like to eat?

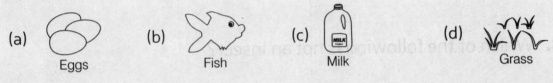

(a) Eggs   (b) Fish   (c) Milk   (d) Grass

15. Animals like lion, tiger always eat _____.

(a) Milk   (b) Flesh   (c) Chapati   (d) Honey

16. Which of the animals can live on both land and water?

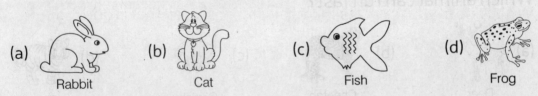

(a) Rabbit   (b) Cat   (c) Fish   (d) Frog

17. Arrange the following letters to find the name of an animal.

RSHEO

(a) HEN   (b) PIGEON   (c) HORSE   (d) PEACOCK

18. Match the animals given in column I with their respective homes given in column II.

	Column I				Column II
(A)	Bird	(i)			Stable
(B)	Honeybee	(ii)			Nest
(C)	Horse	(iii)			Hole
(D)	Mouse	(iv)			Beehive

	(A)	(B)	(C)	(D)
(a)	(iv)	(i)	(iii)	(ii)
(b)	(iii)	(ii)	(iv)	(i)
(c)	(ii)	(iv)	(i)	(iii)
(d)	(iii)	(i)	(ii)	(iv)

19. Which of the following is not true?

(a) Dog guards our home   (b) Deer gives us milk

(c) Sheep gives us wool   (d) Donkey carries load

20. Which of these animals kill other animals for their food?

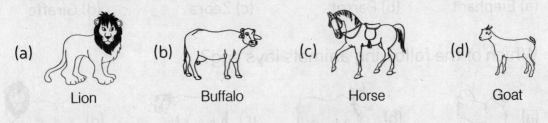

(a) Lion   (b) Buffalo   (c) Horse   (d) Goat

21. Animals have _____ legs and birds have _____ legs.

(a) 2, 4   (b) 6, 4   (c) 4, 2   (d) 4, 4

Arun saw many animals in the zoo. But he forget their names when telling about them to his mother. Help to identify those animals.

Answer the questions (22-24) with the help of given figure above.

22. This animal has no hands or legs and only crawls.

(a) Crocodile   (b) Snake   (c) Monkey   (d) Frog

23. This bird lays egg like hen but swims easily in water.

(a) Duck   (b) Sparrow   (c) Ostrich   (d) Parrot

24. This animal has a tall neck and brown spots on its body.

(a) Elephant   (b) Parrot   (c) Zebra   (d) Giraffe

25. Which of the following animals lays egg?

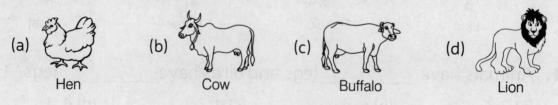

(a) Hen   (b) Cow   (c) Buffalo   (d) Lion

4

Human Beings and Their Needs

1. When you see a cartoon, which sense organ do you use?

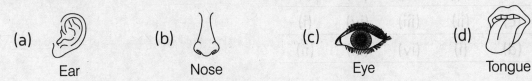

(a) Ear   (b) Nose   (c) Eye   (d) Tongue

2. Your mother is making tasty food. You smell it with _____ .

(a) Eye   (b) Skin   (c) Ear   (d) Nose

3. When we hold a hot cup of tea. We instantly remove our hands. Which sense organ tells us that the tea is hot?

(a) Eye   (b) Skin   (c) Ears   (d) Nose

4. While listening to music, we are using our _____ .

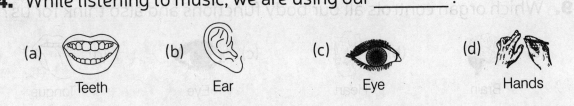

(a) Teeth   (b) Ear   (c) Eye   (d) Hands

5. Match the sense organs given in column I with their functions given in column II.

Column I			Column II	
(A)	Eye	(i)		Smell
(B)	Nose	(ii)		Taste
(C)	Ear	(iii)		Read
(D)	Tongue	(iv)		Hear

	(A)	(B)	(C)	(D)
(a)	(iii)	(i)	(iv)	(ii)
(b)	(iv)	(ii)	(iii)	(i)
(c)	(ii)	(iii)	(iv)	(i)
(d)	(i)	(iv)	(iii)	(ii)

6. The human body has _____ sense organs.

(a) 6   (b) 7   (c) 2   (d) 5

7. Whenever we run, then we are using our _____ .

(a) Eye   (b) Hands   (c) Stomach   (d) Legs

8. Identify the body part.

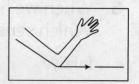

(a) Knee   (b) Leg

(c) Eye   (d) Elbow

9. Which organ controls all our body functions and also think for us?

(a) Brain   (b) Heart   (c) Eye   (d) Tongue

10. Which part of the body is used to cut and chew the food?

(a) Teeth (b) Nose (c) Eye (d) Tongue

11. Fruits and vegetables should always be _____ .

(a) Cut before eating (b) Cooked before eating

(c) Properly washed before eating or cooking (d) Cut before cooking

12. Which of the following is not a healthy food?

(a) Milk (b) Rice and Wheat (c) Eggs (d) Burger

13. Which of these is not true about food?

(a) Food help us to grow (b) Food give us energy to work

(c) Some foods are junk food (d) Junk food is healthy

14. Ravi drank a glass of milk, ate 1 piece of bread, 1 packet of chips and 1 burger for breakfast. Then he ate rice, potato.

Milk Bread Chips Burger Rice

Identify, which foods are not healthy for Ravi?

(a) Milk and Rice (b) Burger and Chips

(c) Rice and Chips (d) Potato and Milk

15. The meal that we take at night is _____ .

(a) Dinner (b) Lunch (c) Breakfast (d) None of these

16. Foods that are obtained from plants is vegetarian food. Which of the following is a vegetarian food?

Tomato Soup   Chicken   Lemon Juice   Eggs

(a) Chicken and Lemon Juice

(b) Eggs and Tomato Soup

(c) Chicken and Eggs

(d) Tomato Soup and Lemon Juice

17. Look at the pictures given below and tell which of the clothes help us to keep warm in winters?

Woollen cap (1)   Raincoat (2)   Woollen socks (3)   Shorts (4)   Sweater (5)   T-shirt (6)

(a) 1, 2 and 4   (b) 4 and 5   (c) 2 and 6   (d) 1, 3 and 5

18. Match the following items given in column I and column II.

Column I		Column II	
(A)	Chapati	(i)	Tree
(B)	Milk	(ii)	Cow
(C)	Apple	(iii)	Wheat

	(A)	(B)	(C)
(a)	(iii)	(ii)	(i)
(b)	(i)	(ii)	(iii)
(c)	(iii)	(i)	(ii)
(d)	(ii)	(iii)	(i)

19. During summers we should wear which type of clothes?

(a) Woollen   (b) Cotton   (c) Silk   (d) Jute

20. Which of the following cloth is needed in rainy season?

(a) Shirt   (b) Jacket   (c) Raincoat and boots   (d) Coat

21. Wool that keep us warm during winters is taken from which animal?

(a) Goat   (b) Sheep   (c) Pig   (d) Elephant

22. Which of the following is true?

(a) Woollen clothes keep us warm

(b) Woollen clothes keep us cool

(c) We wear woollen clothes in summer

(d) We wear woollen clothes in rainy season

23. A good posture while studying is _____.

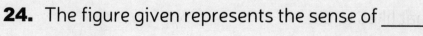

(a)   (b)   (c)   (d)

24. The figure given represents the sense of _____

(a) Smell   (b) Taste

(c) Hearing   (d) Touch

25. Which of the following activity should we do twice a day?

(a) Playing   (b) Brushing   (c) Bathing   (d) Sleeping

26. Label the parts P, Q, R, S respectively.

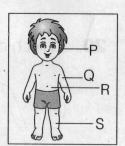

(a) Eye, Nose, Brain, Leg   (b) Nose, Leg, Head, Stomach

(c) Ear, Hand, Stomach, Leg   (d) Eye, Nose, Ear, Head

27. Match the body part in column I that rhymes with the word in column II and select the correct option.

	Column I		Column II
(A)	Ear	(i)	Tail
(B)	Nail	(ii)	Tongue
(C)	Lung	(iii)	Rear
(D)	Eye	(iv)	Thigh

	(A)	(B)	(C)	(D)
(a)	(iii)	(i)	(ii)	(iv)
(b)	(ii)	(iii)	(i)	(iv)
(c)	(iv)	(iii)	(ii)	(i)
(d)	(i)	(ii)	(iii)	(iv)

28. Fill in the blanks to complete the poem :

Two little _____ to look around.

Two little ears to hear each sound.

One little _____ to smell what's sweets.

One little mouth that likes to eat.

(a) eyes, hand   (b) eyes, nose   (c) hands, nose   (d) hands, leg

5

Good Habits, Safety and First Aid

1. Which of the following is not a good habit?

Washing hands before eating	Brushing teeth twice a day	Doing exercises regularly	Getting up late in the morning
(a)	(b)	(c)	(d)

2. Which of the following is used to cut nails?

Comb	Nail Cutter	Toothbrush	Soap
(a)	(b)	(c)	(d)

3. It is a bad habit to _____.

Bath everyday	Wash hands after toilet	Throw things in a dustbin	Plucking flowers and leaves
(a)	(b)	(c)	(d)

4. Match the following.

Column I			Column II	
(A)	Coughing or Sneezing	(i)	Earbud	
(B)	Hair	(ii)	Handkerchief	
(C)	Bath	(iii)	Comb	
(D)	Ear	(iv)	Towel	

	(A)	(B)	(C)	(D)
(a)	(iii)	(i)	(ii)	(iv)
(b)	(i)	(iv)	(iii)	(ii)
(c)	(iv)	(ii)	(i)	(iii)
(d)	(ii)	(iii)	(iv)	(i)

5. What will you say when you pushed someone by mistake?

(a) Sorry   (b) Thank you

(c) Welcome   (d) None of these

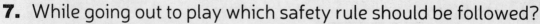

6. What will you say when somebody helped you?

(a) Ok   (b) Sorry

(c) Thank you   (d) Best of luck

7. While going out to play which safety rule should be followed?

(a) Play in the playground

(b) Wear shoes or sandals

(c) Do not push anyone on the swings

(d) All of the above

8. Which of these things are not safe to use by small children?

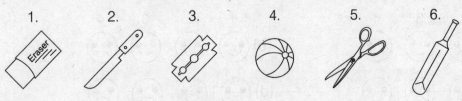

1.   2.   3.   4.   5.   6.

(a) 1, 5 and 6   (b) 2, 3 and 5   (c) 2, 4 and 6   (d) 1, 4 and 6

Direction (9-11) Look at the following picture and answer the following questions.

9. Where should we walk on the road?

(a) Zebra Crossing

(b) Middle of the road

(c) Footpath

(d) None of the above

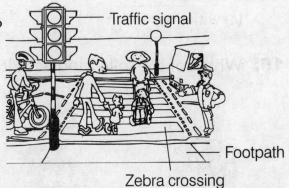

Traffic signal

Footpath

Zebra crossing

10. We should always cross the road from _____ .

(a) Never cross the road   (b) Zebra crossing

(c) Footpath   (d) All of these

11. The three lights of the traffic signal is red, yellow and green. What does the red light indicate?

(a) Wait   (b) Go   (c) Stop   (d) All of these

12. The person standing at the side of the road is _____ .

(a) Traffic Police   (b) Policeman   (c) Sweeper   (d) Army man

13. Draw 😊 if statement is correct and 🙁 if it is incorrect.

1. Do not run on the stairs   2. Never play with fire
3. Jump from a moving bus   4. Play on the road

Codes

```
        1     2     3     4                    1     2     3     4
(a)    😦    😦    😊    😊           (b)    😊    😦    😊    😦

(c)    😦    😊    😦    😊           (d)    😊    😊    😦    😦
```

14. Children should never go into the swimming pool _____ .

(a) alone   (b) with their parents

(c) with their coach   (d) with their teacher

15. Which of the following activity should not be done by the children?

Getting into the bus in a line   Touching electrical gadgets   Obey traffic rules   Hold hands while crossing the road

(a)   (b)   (c)   (d)

16. Which of the following is a correct safety rule?

   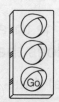

Placing hand outside the bus window   Disturbing the driver   Playing with sharp things   Going when the green light appears

(a)   (b)   (c)   (d)

17. When someone gets injured, we use _____ .

(a) Third Aid   (b) Second Aid   (c) First Aid   (d) None of these

18. We should cross the road when the traffic light is _____ .

(a) Red   (b) Green   (c) Yellow   (d) All of these

19. Identify the things that you put in a First Aid Box?

1	2	3	4	5
Band-Aid	Dettol	Scissors	Toffees	Ball

(a) 2 and 3   (b) 1, 2 and 3

(c) 3, 4 and 5   (d) 4 and 5

20. Which of the following figures shows zebra crossing?

(a)   (b)   (c)   (d)

21. Match the following

	Column I		Column II
(A)	Red light	(i)	Stop
(B)	Green light	(ii)	Move
(C)	Yellow light	(iii)	Ready to move

	(A)	(B)	(C)
(a)	(i)	(ii)	(iii)
(b)	(ii)	(i)	(iii)
(c)	(i)	(iii)	(ii)
(d)	(iii)	(ii)	(i)

6

Air, Water and Weather

1. Which of the following cannot be seen but is present everywhere in the nature?

   (a) Sun   (b) Air   (c) Sky   (d) Water

2. Which of the following do not need air?

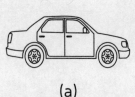  

       (a)   (b)   (c)   (d)

3. Which of the following is not true?

   (a) Air has weight   (b) Air fills space   (c) Air can be seen   (d) Air can be felt

4. Moving air is called _____ .

   (a) Water   (b) Wind   (c) Storm   (d) Smoke

5. Match the following.

	Column I		Column II
(A)	(hot air balloon)	(i)	Fly in the air
(B)	(tree with roots)	(ii)	Dry in the air
(C)	(clothes on a line)	(iii)	Breathe in the air
(D)	(birds flying)	(iv)	Filled with air

	A	B	C	D
(a)	(iii)	(i)	(iv)	(ii)
(b)	(iv)	(iii)	(ii)	(i)
(c)	(i)	(iv)	(iii)	(ii)
(d)	(ii)	(iii)	(i)	(iv)

6. Which picture shows that the day is hot due to hot air?

(a)

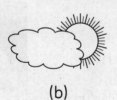

(b)

(c)

(d)

7. Pick the odd one out.

Watering the plants
(a)

Bathing
(b)

Cleaning the floor
(c)

Sleeping
(d)

8. Which of the following makes the air dirty?

(a) Dust   (b) Germs   (c) Smoke   (d) All of these

9. Which of the following is not true?

(a) All livings things drink water   (b) Water has no color

(c) Water is tasteless   (d) All of these are true

10. Which of the following is not a form of water?

(a)   Ice   (b)   Snow   (c)   Rain drops   (d)   Bubbles

11. When water boils then it forms _____ .

(a) Steam   (b) Ice

(c) Rain drops   (d) None of these

12. This is the picture of a river. Which of the following things about this picture is true?

(a) The river water is dirty.

(b) The river is full of garbage.

(c) People throw waste material into the river.

(d) All of these are true

13. In which season days are very cold?

(a) Summer   (b) Rainy   (c) Winter   (d) All of these

14. Which of the following things is needed in hot day?

(a) Cold drinks   (b) Fan, AC, Cooler

(c) Cotton Clothes   (d) All of these

15. Match the following.

Column I		Column II
(A) ![sun]	(i)	Rainy
(B) ![cloud]	(ii)	Sunny
(C) ![rain cloud]	(iii)	Windy
(D) ![windy tree]	(iv)	Cloudy

	A	B	C	D
(a)	(i)	(iii)	(iv)	(ii)
(b)	(iii)	(i)	(ii)	(iv)
(c)	(ii)	(iv)	(i)	(iii)
(d)	(iv)	(iii)	(iii)	(i)

Direction (16-17) Look at the following weather chart and answer the questions.

Day	Monday	Tuesday	Wednesday	Thursday
Morning	![cloud]	![windy tree]	![rain cloud]	![sun]
Afternoon	![rain cloud]	![cloud]	![sun]	![sun]

16. According to the weather report which day is windy and cloudy?

(a) Monday   (b) Thursday   (c) Tuesday   (d) Wednesday

17. According to the weather report which is the hottest day?

(a) Thursday   (b) Monday   (c) Wednesday   (d) Tuesday

7

The Sky

1. Which of the following things can be seen in the sky?

(a)
Sun

(b)
Star

(c)
Moon

(d) All of these

2. What is the shape of the Sun?

(a)

(b)

(c)

(d)

3. Which of the following statement about Sun is not true?

(a) Sun gives us heat

(b) Sun shines at night

(c) Sun gives us light

(d) Sun shines during the day

4. Rising, Rising the sun is rising. Going, Going Darkness is going. The Sun rises from which direction?

(a) West   (b) South   (c) East   (d) North

5. Very big and bright ball of fire in the sky is known as _____ .

    (a) Sun   (b) Moon   (c) North Star   (d) None of these

6. The sun sets in the _____ .

    (a) East   (b) North   (c) South   (d) West

7. Identify the things that can be seen in the night sky.

    (a) Sun   (b) Moon   (c) Stars   (d) Both (b) and (c)

8. Every night it can be seen in a different shape. What is it?

    (a) River   (b) Moon   (c) Mountain   (d) Sky

9. Match the following.

	Column I		Column II
(A)	🌙	1.	Half moon
(B)	⚪	2.	No moon
(C)	◗	3.	Full moon
(D)	▦	4.	Quarter moon

Codes

    A B C D   A B C D
(a) 3 2 4 1   (b) 4 3 1 2
(c) 2 1 4 3   (d) 1 4 3 2

10. The shape of the quarter moon is also known as _____ .

(a) Diamond   (b) Triangle   (c) Semi-circle   (d) Crescent

11. Which of the following shape is never taken by the Moon?

(a)   (b)   (c)   (d)

12. This is a vehicle that can take you to the Moon. What is it called?

(a) Helicopter   (b) Parachute   (c) Rocket   (d) Aeroplane

13. Can you count the number of stars in the Night sky?

(a) Yes, I can count   (b) Yes, it is 100

(c) May be more than 100   (d) No, it is not possible

14. Identify the shape in which the stars appear to us.

(a)   (b)   (c)   (d)

15. Where do all plants, land and water animals and humans live?

(a) Sun   (b) Earth   (c) Star   (d) Moon

16. Which of the following is closer to earth?

(a) Moon   (b) Sun   (c) Star   (d) None of these

Practice Set 1

A Test Based on the Whole Content

1. Which of the following pictures show both a living and a non-living things together?

   (a)

   Fish in a fish bowl

   (b)

   Pencil in a pencil box

   (c)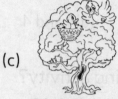

   Birds living on a tree

   (d)

   Water in a bottle

2. Ravi got a teddy bear  and a little puppy  on his birthday. In his next birthday what will happen?

   (a) Teddy bear will grow   (b) Both will grow
   (c) Little puppy will grow   (d) None of these

3. Write the type of plants shown below.

   A   B   C   D

   A   B   C   D   A   B   C   D
   (a) Tree Herb Creeper Shrub   (b) Creeper Climber Tree Herb
   (c) Herb Shrub Climber Creeper (d) Creeper Shrub Climber Herb

4. Which of the following animal does not live in forest?

   (a) Deer   (b) Lion   (c) Rabbit   (d) Penguin

5. Neem, Tulsi are some plants that give us which of the following?

(a)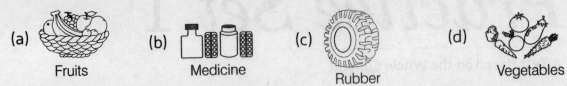
Fruits

(b)
Medicine

(c)
Rubber

(d)
Vegetables

6. Which of the following is true?

1. Tiger eats grass and leaves.
2. Crocodile lives on both land and water.
3. Pet animals live in forest.
4. Baby of a lion is called a cub.

(a) 2 and 4   (b) 1 and 3   (c) 2 and 3   (d) 1 and 4

7. Ankit is using which sense organs to do the following activity?

(a)
Ears and Nose

(b)
Eyes and Ears

(c)
Tongue and Nose

(d)
Skin and Tongue

8. Which of the following fruits have a large number of seeds in it?

(a)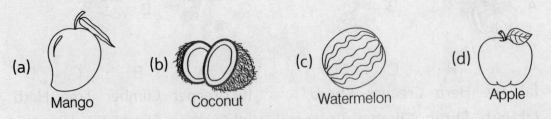
Mango

(b)
Coconut

(c)
Watermelon

(d)
Apple

9. A large part of our body contains _____ .

(a) air   (b) water   (c) air and water   (d) water vapour

10. Match the following.

	Column I		Column II
(A)		(i)	Doing Exercises
(B)		(ii)	Cutting nails
(C)		(iii)	Brushing teeth
(D)		(iv)	Washing hands

	A	B	C	D
(a)	(i)	(iv)	(iii)	(ii)
(b)	(iii)	(iv)	(ii)	(i)
(c)	(ii)	(i)	(iv)	(iii)
(d)	(iv)	(iii)	(i)	(ii)

11. See the following pictures and find out which statement is true?

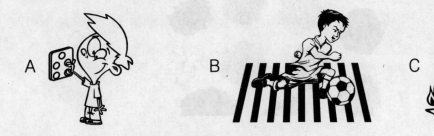

A   B   C

(a) They all are following safety rules.

(b) Boy in C is following safety rule.

(c) Boy in A is following safety rule.

(d) They all are not following safety rule.

12. What is filled inside all of these?

Swimming Tube

Balloon

Football

Tyre

(a) Water   (b) Gun   (c) Air   (d) None of these

13. We should keep the rivers clean because _____.

1. All living beings drink water from it.
2. Dirty water pollutes the river.

(a) Only 1   (b) Both 1 and 2   (c) Only 2   (d) None of these

14. Which of the following is man made non-living thing?

(a)
Moon

(b)
Umbrella

(c)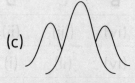
Mountain

(d)
Sun

15. Which of the following about seeds is not true?

(a) New plants grow from seeds

(b) Some seeds are eaten by humans

(c) Some plants can grow without seeds

(d) None of the above

16. Classify the following into plant and animal products.

Animal Food	Plant Food
(a) Idli, Honey, Bread	Butter, Fruit, Juice
(b) Fruit, Juice, Butter	Idli, Bread, Honey
(c) Bread, Idli	Butter, Fruit, Juice, Honey
(d) Butter, Honey	Idli, Fruit, Juice, Bread

17. Mark 😊 for correct statement and 🙁 for incorrect statement.

1. Air and water are living things.
2. We should save water.
3. We should keep the air clean.

    I   II   III   I   II   III
(a) 😊 😊 😊   (b) 🙁 😊 😊
(c) 🙁 😊 😊   (d) 😊 🙁 🙁

18. Which picture is not matched correctly?

(a) ⬤   (b) 🌙   (c) ◗   (d) ☆

  Full Moon   Crescent Moon   Half Moon   Quarter Moon

19. Fill in the blanks by choosing the correct option :
We should drink _____ water. Drinking _____ water can cause many _____ .

(a) pure, pure, diseases   (b) impure, pure, diseases
(c) pure, impure, diseases   (d) impure, impure, diseases

20. Which of the following is true?

(a) Air is red in color
(b) Air is sweet in taste
(c) Sometimes air is hot and sometimes it is cold
(d) Air is not present everywhere

Practice Set 2

A Test Based on the Whole Content

1. Pick the odd one out.

 (a)   (b)    (c)    (d)

2. Consider the following statements which is correct?

1. All living things move by itself.
2. Plants are living things.

(a) Only 1 is correct

(b) Only 2 is correct

(c) Both 1 and 2 are correct

(d) Both 1 and 2 are incorrect

3. What is the function of label A in the given figure?

(a) Hold the plant to the ground

(b) Contain seed for growth of new plants

(c) Makes food for the plant

(d) None of the above

4. Consider the following two statements. Which of the statement is correct?

1. Animals like cow, goat, buffalo give us milk.
2. All animals do not give us milk.

(a) Only 1 is correct

(b) Only 2 is correct

(c) Both 1 and 2 are correct

(d) Both 1 and 2 are incorrect

5. Match the animals given in column I with the things we get from them in column II.

	Column I		Column II
(A)		(i)	
(B)		(ii)	
(C)		(iii)	
(D)		(iv)	

	(A)	**(B)**	**(C)**	**(D)**
(a)	(i)	(ii)	(iii)	(iv)
(b)	(iv)	(iii)	(ii)	(i)
(c)	(iii)	(iv)	(i)	(ii)
(d)	(ii)	(i)	(iv)	(iii)

6. Nikita eats chips and pizzafull, how will it affect her?

(a) She will be healthy   (b) She will not be healthy

(c) Both of these   (d) None of these

7. These clothes are required in which season?

(a) Summer   (b) Autumn   (c) Winter   (d) Rainy

8. Pick the odd one out.

Play on
the road
(a)

Get off a
moving bus
(b)

Crossing at
zebra crossing
(c)

Placing hand outside
the bus window
(d)

9. What is first aid?

(a) First treatment given to a patient

(b) Giving food to hungry people

(c) Looking after animals

(d) Helping the sick people

10. When we keep water in the freezer then the water forms _____ .

(a)
Steam

(b)
Ice

(c)
Snow

(d)
Water

11. All living things need _____, _____ and Food to live.

(a) Air, Water

(b) Day, Night

(c) Chips, Chocolate

(d) Sea, Land

12. Match the following.

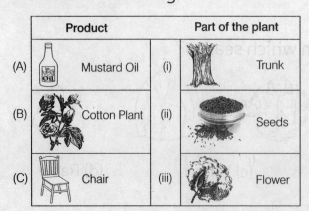

Product		Part of the plant	
(A)	Mustard Oil	(i)	Trunk
(B)	Cotton Plant	(ii)	Seeds
(C)	Chair	(iii)	Flower

	(A)	(B)	(C)
(a)	(ii)	(iii)	(i)
(b)	(iii)	(ii)	(i)
(c)	(i)	(ii)	(iii)
(d)	(ii)	(i)	(iii)

13. Raju stood in front of the window and saw the sun rising. In which direction is his window?

(a) East   (b) North   (c) West   (d) South

14. What are these?

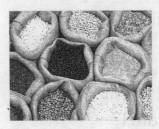

(a) Spices   (b) Fruits   (c) Dry fruits   (d) Pulses

15. Which of the following foods should be taken daily?

(a)   (b)   (c)   (d)

Sweets   Chips   Milk   Noodles

16. Match the animals given is column I with their respective voice given in column II.

	Column I		Column II
(A)	 Lion	(i)	Bark
(B)	Cat	(ii)	Moo
(C)		(iii)	Roar
(D)	Cow	(iv)	Meow

	(A)	(B)	(C)	(D)
(a)	(i)	(ii)	(iii)	(iv)
(b)	(iv)	(iii)	(ii)	(i)
(c)	(iii)	(iv)	(i)	(ii)
(d)	(ii)	(iv)	(iii)	(i)

17. *I will look like a Duck when I will grow up.* Who am I?

(a) Chick   (b) Puppy

(c) Kitten   (d) Duckling

18. Which of the following should not be done while crossing the road?

    1. Using zebra crossing   2. Talking on the mobile

    3. Running   4. Listening to music

    (a) Only 1   (b) Only 2 and 3

    (c) 2, 3 and 4   (d) Only 1 and 2

19. How much days does it take for a full moon to become a no moon?

    (a) 7 days   (b) 10 days

    (c) 14 days   (d) 5 days

20. Select the incorrect matching pair.

Festival	Celebration
(a) Holi	Spring
(b) Diwali	Summer
(c) Lohri	Winter
(d) Teej	Rainy

Answers

Chapter 1 : Living and Non-Living Things

1. (c)	2. (c)	3. (a)	4. (a)	5. (c)
6. (b)	7. (d)	8. (b)	9. (c)	10. (d)
11. (c)	12. (a)	13. (c)	14. (c)	15. (d)
16. (d)	17. (c)	18. (a)	19. (d)	20. (b)
21. (a)	22. (c)	23. (b)	24. (c)	25. (b)
26. (d)				

Chapter 2 : Plants

1. (c)	2. (c)	3. (a)	4. (b)	5. (d)
6. (c)	7. (a)	8. (d)	9. (c)	10. (b)
11. (b)	12. (d)	13. (d)	14. (b)	15. (d)
16. (a)	17. (b)	18. (c)	19. (a)	20. (c)
21. (c)				

Chapter 3 : Animals

1. (d)	2. (a)	3. (d)	4. (c)	5. (a)
6. (c)	7. (b)	8. (c)	9. (b)	10. (a)
11. (d)	12. (c)	13. (c)	14. (d)	15. (b)
16. (d)	17. (c)	18. (c)	19. (b)	20. (a)
21. (c)	22. (b)	23. (a)	24. (d)	25. (a)

Chapter 4 : Human Beings and Their Needs

1. (c)	2. (d)	3. (b)	4. (b)	5. (a)
6. (d)	7. (d)	8. (d)	9. (a)	10. (a)
11. (c)	12. (d)	13. (d)	14. (b)	15. (a)
16. (d)	17. (d)	18. (a)	19. (b)	20. (c)
21. (b)	22. (a)	23. (a)	24. (d)	25. (b)
26. (c)	27. (a)	28. (b)		

Chapter 5 : Good Habits, Safety and First Aid

1. (d)	2. (b)	3. (d)	4. (d)	5. (a)
6. (c)	7. (d)	8. (b)	9. (c)	10. (b)
11. (c)	12. (a)	13. (d)	14. (a)	15. (b)
16. (d)	17. (c)	18. (b)	19. (b)	20. (a)
21. (a)				

Chapter 6 : Air, Water and Weather

1. (b)	2. (a)	3. (c)	4. (b)	5. (b)
6. (c)	7. (d)	8. (d)	9. (d)	10. (d)
11. (a)	12. (d)	13. (c)	14. (d)	15. (c)
16. (c)	17. (a)			

Chapter 7 : The Sky

1. (d)	2. (c)	3. (b)	4. (c)	5. (a)
6. (d)	7. (d)	8. (b)	9. (b)	10. (d)
11. (a)	12. (c)	13. (d)	14. (c)	15. (b)
16. (a)				

Practice Set 1

1. (a)	2. (c)	3. (d)	4. (d)	5. (b)
6. (a)	7. (b)	8. (c)	9. (b)	10. (b)
11. (d)	12. (c)	13. (b)	14. (b)	15. (d)
16. (d)	17. (c)	18. (d)	19. (c)	20. (c)

Practice Set 2

1. (d)	2. (c)	3. (c)	4. (c)	5. (c)
6. (b)	7. (c)	8. (c)	9. (a)	10. (b)
11. (a)	12. (a)	13. (a)	14. (d)	15. (c)
16. (c)	17. (d)	18. (c)	19. (c)	20. (b)